# SING A SONG OF SIXPENCE

Sing a song of sixpence,
A pocket full of rye;
Four and twenty blackbirds
Baked in a pie.

4

# Goodnight

## STORIES and RHYMES

**Brown Watson**
ENGLAND

When the pie was opened,
The birds began to sing;
Wasn't that a dainty dish
To set before the King.

The King was in his counting house
Counting out his money;
The Queen was in the parlour
Eating bread and honey.

The maid was in the garden
Hanging out the clothes;
When down came a blackbird
And pecked off her nose.

# TWO LITTLE DICKIE BIRDS

Two little dickie birds sitting on a wall,
One named Peter,
One named Paul.

Fly away, Peter!
Fly away, Paul!
Come back, Peter!
Come back, Paul!

# TO MARKET, TO MARKET

To market, to market,
To buy a fat pig,
Home again, home again,
Jiggety jig.

To market, to market,
To buy a fat hog,
Home again, home again,
Jiggety jog.

11

# POLLY PUT THE KETTLE ON

Polly put the kettle on,
Polly put the kettle on,
Polly put the kettle on,
We'll all have tea.

Sukey take it off again,
Sukey take it off again,
Sukey take it off again,
They've all gone away.

# TINKER, TAILOR

Tinker, tailor,
Soldier, sailor,
Rich man, poor man,
Beggar man, thief.

# PAT-A-CAKE

Pat-a-cake, pat-a-cake, baker's man,
Bake me a cake as fast as you can;
Pat it and prick it and mark it with B,
And put it in the oven for baby and me.

16

# The Witch's Cat

What's your idea of a witch's cat? A cat like me, perhaps – black, with sharp, pointed ears, big eyes and a long tail? And the witch? Well, you probably wouldn't expect her to be forgetful and stupid, getting into all sorts of muddles and screaming "Willow!" at the sight of a mouse – would you?

But then, you probably don't know my mistress, Wumpet the Witch! I heard her say once that she got her name from a spell which had gone wrong…. And, with Wumpet around, that's nothing unusual!

"Wee-wee-willow-wickety... er ... Wicky-won-wackety..." (Wumpet has never ever quite managed to remember the right words for a spell, yet!) "Or, is it Winny-wack-williby?" No wonder her magic gets all mixed up!

I can usually see when spells are starting to go wrong, long before Wumpet does. That's how it is that I always manage to get out of the way in time, and she doesn't! But, whether I hide under the stairs, or up in the attic, Wumpet is never far away! So you can guess how pleased I was to find a hole in the fence, just big enough for me to squeeze through.

"Hello," said a voice, not a bit like Wumpet's. "You're the cat from next door, aren't you?"

Without thinking, I mewed at her, "Yes, that's right," hoping she would understand. And, she did!

What's more, she seemed to know about Wumpet, too.

"I've seen you with that silly old witch," she said and stroked my head. "Would you like one of my cheese crackers?"

Cheese crackers! I had never tasted
cheese crackers in my whole life!
Then she brought me a saucer of
rich, creamy milk and an old
blanket, in case I wanted to lie
down.

"Don't forget that isn't our cat. He really belongs to someone else," came another voice.

Jenny laughed. "He is just like a friend come round to play, Mummy. That's all right, isn't it?"

And, so it was. Jenny never once said a word about Wumpet, or about me being a witch's cat. That was just one of our little secrets. If Wumpet only knew how we laughed at her.

And what with all the snacks Jenny kept feeding me, I was getting fatter and fatter – which meant the hole in the fence got bigger and bigger, until even Wumpet could see it.

Of course, I squeezed back through
the hole as quickly as I could, but it
was too late!

"So!" she screeched in her loud,
witchy sort of voice. "This is where
you go when my back is turned, eh?"

She stamped back indoors, and
came out waving a rolling-pin!
"My magic wand!" she said with a
wild cackle. "Now I can get one of
my spells working on this."
Jenny and I held our breath.

She straightened her pointed hat and began to sing.

"Minny-mon-moony. Cold ginger beer! Great big hole, please disappear!"

Then, she turned round three times.

Poor old Wumpet! She didn't realise she had holes in her skirt and her magic made the holes disappear, until there was no skirt left! But the hole in the fence was still as big as it had ever been....

Next day, we watched Wumpet dragging out her cauldron.

"Magic potion!" she kept puffing to herself. "That's what I need!" She gave a snort in our direction, but we pretended not to notice.

"Dandelion and daisy root! Lollipop sticks and football boot! Hair of maggot, slice of rain! Put my fence to rights, again!" It seemed that this time, Wumpet had actually got the words right for once!

And can you guess what happened next? Nothing at all! All day long and half the night Wumpet kept on with that spell, getting angrier and angrier. The words became more muddled each time.

"Wonder what she's going to do next?" said Jenny. She was trying hard not to laugh out loud, but it wasn't easy – not when we could see Wumpet getting tangled up in armfuls of long twigs and more spell books!

Wumpet took a long twig and drew a circle in the soil.

"Circle and square, drawn here today, please make the hole in the fence go away!"

"Drat!" she shouted. "Drat, drat!"

"Is that part of the spell?" Jenny and I giggled helplessly.

"Drat!" Wumpet screamed again. "I forgot to dip the stick in the juice of a red jelly-bean! I'll have to go and fetch one!"

By now, Jenny was laughing so much that her Daddy came out to see what was happening.

"Er, it's the cat from next door," said Jenny hastily. "He looks so funny, squeezing through the fence."

"Yes, Mummy did mention it. I'll fetch my tools, Jenny, then we can patch it up with a bit of wood. Don't suppose the old lady next door has noticed it," he remarked, as he sawed and hammered.

When Wumpet came out again and saw that the fence had been mended, she gave a whoop of delight. "My magic worked, after all!" she cackled. "One of my best spells! Kippers for tea tonight, Willow!"

Now, when I want to see Jenny, I must climb up over the fence! But, of course, Wumpet doesn't know anything about that. She is too busy working on some more of her wonderful magic spells!

## CLAP HANDS

Clap hands, clap hands,
'Til Daddy comes home.
He will bring goodies
For baby alone.

# DIDDLE, DIDDLE, DUMPLING

Diddle, diddle, dumpling, my son John,
Went to bed with his trousers on;
One shoe off and one shoe on,
Diddle, diddle, dumpling, my son John.

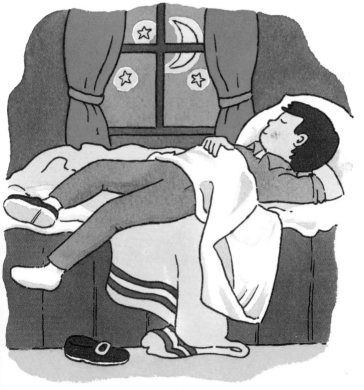

# THREE BLIND MICE

Three blind mice, three blind mice,
See how they run, see how they run!
They all ran after the farmer's wife,

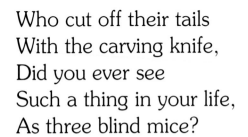

Who cut off their tails
With the carving knife,
Did you ever see
Such a thing in your life,
As three blind mice?

# JACK AND JILL

Jack and Jill went up the hill,
To fetch a pail of water;
Jack fell down and broke his crown,
And Jill came tumbling after.

# THE MAN IN THE MOON

The man in the moon,
Came down too soon,
And asked the way to Norwich.
He went by the south,
And burned his mouth,
By eating cold plum porridge.

# ONE, TWO, BUCKLE MY SHOE

One, two, buckle my shoe;
Three, four, knock at the door;
Five, six, pick up sticks;
Seven, eight, lay them straight;

48

Nine, ten, my fat hen;

Eleven, twelve,
dig and delve;

# SOLOMON GRUNDY

Solomon Grundy,
Born on Monday,
Christened on Tuesday,
Married on Wednesday,
Took ill on Thursday,

Worse on Friday,
Died on Saturday,
Buried on Sunday,
And that was the end
Of Solomon Grundy.

# PUSSY CAT, PUSSY CAT

Pussy cat, pussy cat,
Where have you been?
I've been up to London,
To visit the Queen.

Pussy cat, pussy cat,
What did you there?
I frightened a little mouse,
Under a chair.

# Teddy's
# Birthday Surprise

Teddy Bear woke up, blinking at the sun shining into his room. The birds sang and chattered noisily. Downstairs, Mummy and Daddy Bear laughed and talked together. But why did it feel such a special sort of day?

"My birthday!" he remembered, jumping out of bed.

He hoped he would have lots of birthday cards, and Mummy and Daddy always let him open his presents at breakfast-time.

"Happy Birthday, Teddy!" called Mummy Bear.

"Many happy returns!" smiled Daddy. Teddy said nothing. There was one card beside his plate, but no presents – not even from Uncle Sailor Bill. And he never forgot birthdays!

"Cheer up!" smiled Daddy Bear.
"You might have a special birthday
surprise later on."
"A birthday party?" cried Teddy.
"Like last year?"

He had loved blowing up lots of
balloons and hanging them all
around the room. But Mummy
shook her head. "No, Teddy," she
said. "Not a birthday party."

"Maybe Mummy and Daddy haven't enough money to spend on parties and birthdays," thought Teddy.
He opened the card, and up popped a little bear, smiling and waving at him!

60

"That's your first birthday surprise," laughed Daddy.
Teddy Bear did like the card! He took it out into the garden, opening and closing it again and again.

Suddenly, he saw his friend Barry Bear. "Hello, Barry!" he cried. "It's my birthday today, and I've got..." "Can't stop, Teddy!" Barry called back. "See you later!"

Teddy couldn't help being surprised. Where COULD Barry be going in such a hurry that he didn't have time to stop and talk? He had never done such a thing before.

Teddy was about to go back indoors, when he saw Teacher Bear carrying a basket and two shopping bags. They looked very heavy.

"Do you need any help, Teacher Bear?" he asked.

"Er – no thank you, Teddy," she said quickly. "I – I think I can manage." And off she went down the road just as fast as she could.

Teddy Bear was very surprised all over again.

Next minute, the sparrows and
robins flew down and began
pecking at some sausage roll
crumbs on the ground. Teddy knew
that they must have fallen from

Teacher Bear's basket.

"I wonder where Teacher Bear was taking those sausage rolls?" thought Teddy. He loved sausage rolls! He was still wondering when he heard voices by the back gate.

It was Honey Bear and Tiny Bear!
"Hurry up, you two," said Honey's
mummy, "or we won't get it all
finished in time!"
"Get WHAT finished in time?"
Teddy wanted to know.

But they just went past. Honey
Bear's mummy was pushing her
shopping trolley with a big box on
top. By now, Teddy was sure
something was going on, something
he didn't know about.

Then he heard voices whispering his name!

"Is that you, Billy Bear?" he called out. And sure enough, the cheeky face of Billy Bear peeped out from behind a big tree.

"Oh – er, hello, Teddy," he said.
"We were all just going somewhere, weren't we, Bella?" Bella was Billy's little sister.
"What have you got behind your back?" asked Teddy.

"Me?" said Billy. "Nothing!" And he and Bella ran off just as fast as they could go!

"Hey!" shouted Teddy, loud enough for Mummy and Daddy to hear. "Come back!"

"What's wrong?" asked Mummy.
"I just don't know!" sighed Teddy.
And he told them all that had
happened. "Billy and Bella wouldn't
even say where they were going!"
he finished.

"Why don't we go the same way?" Daddy Bear suggested. "We might find out, then."
So, they went along the path. Suddenly, Teddy saw something through the trees...

It was a bunch of balloons, bobbing in the breeze, with streamers and paper lanterns!
Then came the sound of a guitar and voices began to sing, "Happy Birthday to You!"

"Happy Birthday, dear Teddy! Happy Birthday to you!" Teddy was so surprised, he couldn't speak! All his friends were there, even Uncle Sailor Bill!

"Mummy had your birthday cake when you saw us!" laughed Honey. "Teacher Bear made the sausage rolls, and Tiny and I brought the balloons!"

"And look at all your presents!" smiled Barry Bear.

"It's a birthday picnic with games to follow!" said Mummy. "We will all have such fun!"

"What do you think, Teddy?"
"Well," said Teddy, "I've already
had lots of surprises today. But
THIS is the best birthday surprise
of all!" And, so it was.

# I HAD A LITTLE NUT TREE

I had a little nut tree,
Nothing would it bear
But a silver nutmeg
And a golden pear.

The King of Spain's daughter
Came to visit me,
And all for the sake
Of my little nut tree.

## GOOSEY GANDER

Goosey, goosey gander,
Where shall I wander?
Upstairs and downstairs,
In my lady's chamber.

Where I met an old man,
Who wouldn't say his prayers,
I took him by the left leg,
And threw him down the stairs.

# MARY, MARY

Mary, Mary, quite contrary,
How does your garden grow?
With silver bells and cockle shells
And pretty maids all in a row.

# RIDE A COCK-HORSE

Ride a cock-horse to Banbury Cross,
To see a fine lady upon a white horse;
Rings on her fingers and bells on her toes,
She shall have music wherever she goes.

# THE NORTH WIND
# DOTH BLOW

The north wind doth blow,
And we shall have snow,
And what will poor robin do then,
Poor thing?

He'll sit in a barn,
And keep himself warm,
And hide his head under his wing,
Poor thing.

# EENSY, WEENSY SPIDER

Eensy, weensy spider,
Climbed the water spout.
Down came the rain
And washed the spider out.

# GO TO BED LATE

Go to bed late,
Stay very small;
Go to bed early,
Grow very tall.

# LITTLE POLLY FLINDERS

Little Polly Flinders
Sat among the cinders,
Warming her pretty little toes;

Her mother came and caught her,
And whipped her little daughter
For spoiling her nice new clothes.

# BAA, BAA, BLACK SHEEP

Baa, baa, black sheep,
Have you any wool?
Yes, sir, yes, sir,
Three bags full.

One for the master,
And one for the dame,
And one for the little boy
Who lives down the lane.

93

## Index